There are 6 books in all which will take your child from age 3 until Primary One. Younger children won't necessarily understand all the stories. That's fine, they don't have to. Learning to **HOLD HANDS** and **WAIT** are the key points, the rest will come in time.

It's never too early for a child to get into good road safety habits that will last them a lifetime. So make sure they're following the best possible example and Go Safe every time you cross.

All that's left to say is – enjoy!

The books support Curriculum for Excellence.

Children can follow Ziggy's adventures online at: **www.gosafewithziggy.com**

Shout 'Zab-a-Ding-a-Doo' to Ziggy!

Today Ziggy is going on a
journey to visit Granny Walker.

Let's see if he can
Go Safe
in the countryside.

Mum, Andrew, Maggie, Ziggy
(and Sausage, of course!)
are going to stay with
Granny Walker in the countryside
for the weekend.

Ziggy can't wait to see the
different animals that live
in the countryside.

He might see a **giraffe.**

Or a **zebra.**

Or maybe even an **elephant!**

It's not a very nice day,
so Mum says that they should
leave for Granny's before
the weather gets any worse.

Ziggy is eager to get going and
as soon as Mum opens the car door
he jumps into the nearest car seat.

'Wahhhhhhhhhhhhhh,'

shrieks Maggie.

'Ziggy's in my car seat.'

'It's ok,' says Mum.
**'Ziggy didn't know that everyone
has their own car seat.'**

Ziggy nods.

He didn't know that.

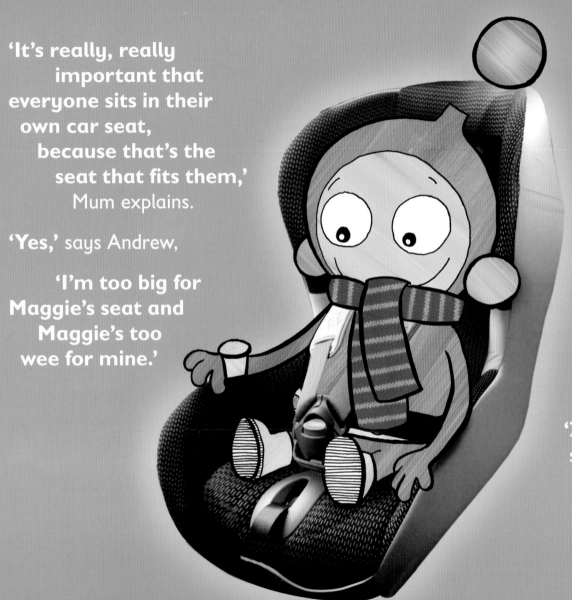

'It's really, really important that everyone sits in their own car seat, because that's the seat that fits them,' Mum explains.

'Yes,' says Andrew,

'I'm too big for Maggie's seat and Maggie's too wee for mine.'

'And you're just right for your seat,' says Mum and shows Ziggy his car seat.

'Zab-a-Ding-a-Doo!' shrieks Ziggy.

On Ziggy's planet, Rocket Captains are the only ones who get special car seats.

Ziggy pushes the button on his car seat, after Mum clicks him in.

'It's really dangerous to fiddle with your car seat, Ziggy!' says Andrew crossly as Mum secures it back in.

Ziggy nods, but he doesn't really know why it's dangerous.

Silly, silly, silly, silly, silly, silly, silly, silly Ziggy.

cLICK

I bet you know why it's dangerous to play with your car seat, don't you?

They haven't been driving very long when suddenly the car skids on an icy bit of road.

'Whoa!'

gasps Ziggy as his whole body jolts forward. Luckily, he's really secure in his car seat and his seatbelt pulls him back.

'Everyone ok?'

Mum asks.

'Phew-wizz,'

says Ziggy, glad he's in his nice safe car seat with his nice safe seatbelt.

Andrew, Maggie and
   Ziggy cheer when they arrive
   at Granny Walker's house.

They give Granny Walker
   a huge kiss then tuck into
a yummy bowl of
      homemade soup.

**Yum, yum,
   yum, yum,
      yum.**

Granny Walker knows loads of great songs:

Ally Bally Bee

Bonnie Wee Jeannie McColl

And You Cannae Shove your Granny off a Bus.

Ziggy loves all the songs but can't understand why anyone would want to shove their granny off a bus.

Grannies are lovely.

And they make great soup.

The next day Andrew, Maggie
and Ziggy get up nice and early
to help Granny make porridge.

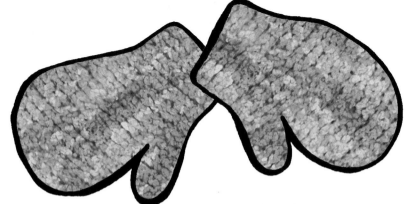

'**What do you fancy doing today?**'
asks Granny Walker.

'**Ziggy wants to see the animals,**'
Maggie says.

'**That's a good idea,**'
says Granny Walker.
'**Wrap up nice and warm and
we'll go for a wee walk.**'

'**Zab-a-Ding-a-Doo!**'
says Ziggy.

Ziggy puts his scarf on and is ready to go,
but the same can't be said of Andrew
and Maggie.

'Mum, I can't find my hat and gloves,'
moans Maggie.

'Mum, I can't find my scarf and wellies,'
moans Andrew.

But Super-Mummy sorts them out.
As usual!

At last, they're ready to go.

But then it's Ziggy's turn to hold everyone up.

'Granny!' calls Ziggy as they get to the gate. **'I can't find the pavement!'**

'We don't have many pavements in the country,' explains Granny Walker.

'That's why we've got to hold hands all the way,' says Maggie.

'And walk so the traffic is driving towards us,' says Andrew.

'Ooh, that sounds scaaaaaaaaaaaaaaaary,' says Ziggy.

'Promise it's not,' says Andrew. 'We need to look out for cars so we can stand in a bit when they drive past. We couldn't do that if we had our backs to them, could we?'

'No,' says Ziggy wondering if one day he'll know as much as Andrew.

Ziggy sees lots of fantastic animals on his walk.

'Hello cows!'

'Hello horses!'

'Hello sheep!'

'Hello very-strange-beast-with-two-sticky-out-horn-things-and-shaggy-orange-hair-that-goes-over-your-eyes.'

'You definitely need to have your fringe trimmed!'

'That's a **Muckle Coo,**' says Granny Walker.

'**Have you never seen a
Highland Cow** before Ziggy?'

'**No,**' says Ziggy.
'**I'm going to take a photo to show my friends.**'

'**How about we walk down to the village shops and
get you a Muckle Coo postcard to send to your wee pals?**'

'**Zab-a-Ding-a-Doo!**' says Ziggy.

They walk down to the village.
Ziggy still hasn't seen

any giraffes.
Or any zebras.
Or any elephants.

Where could they be?

Ziggy decides that they must live near
the shops. Because if you eat
as much as an elephant then
you'd have to really, wouldn't you?

'We have to cross over
   to get to the village,'
   says Granny Walker.

'Do you know what
   we have to do first?'

'Find a
   safe place
   to cross,'
   says Andrew.

'Clever boy!'
   says Granny Walker.

'**Is this a safe place to cross?**'
asks Ziggy.

'**It is, isn't it Granny?**'
says Andrew.
'**Because we can see
the traffic and the traffic
can see us.**'

'**That's right, son. So now
we've found a safe place to
cross, what do we have to do?**'

*Do you know what everyone has
to do once they've found a safe
place to cross? Can you whisper
it in Ziggy's ear?*

'I know!' says Ziggy excitedly.

'We always have
to **WAIT**
before we
cross the road!'

'That's right,
wee yin,'
says Granny Walker.

'We always
have to wait
until it's safe
to cross.'

'Now what do we do when we're crossing the road?
Asks Granny

'Hold hands!' says Ziggy.

'Look for traffic!' says Maggie.

'Listen for traffic!' says Andrew.

'You've done this before, haven't you?' laughs Granny Walker.

No traffic coming so it's safe to cross.

**Everyone holds hands,
looks for traffic,
listens for traffic
and crosses safely.**

'Zab-a-Ding-a-Doo!'
squeals Ziggy and gives
Maggie and Andrew
a big high five.

'Daz-a-Zoo-a-Ding!'
says Maggie,
not getting it quite right.

They walk a wee bit further,
'Look' says Andrew.
**'There's a zebra
crossing down
the road.'**

'At last!'
squeals Ziggy.
**'I'm going to see
a real life zebra!'**

But it isn't a real life
zebra of course!

**'A zebra crossing
helps us to
cross the
road safely'**
explains Maggie.

**'We wait behind the
kerb until the traffic
stops and it's safe
to cross.'**

*Can you see why it's called
a zebra crossing?*

Ziggy can't
stop laughing.

He thought he'd
actually see a real
zebra crossing
the road!

Silly Ziggy!

Granny Walker's Songs

Bonnie Wee Jeannie McColl

A fine wee lass, a bonnie wee lass,
is bonnie wee Jeannie McColl;
I gave her my mother's
engagement ring
and a bonnie wee
tartan shawl.
I met her at a waddin'
in the Co-operative Hall
I wis the best
man and she was the
belle of the ball.

Ally Bally Bee

Ally, bally, ally bally bee,
Sittin' on yer mammy's knee.
Greetin' for a wee bawbee,
Tae buy some Coulter's candy.

You Cannae Shove Your Granny aff a Bus

You cannae shove
your granny aff a bus,
Oh you cannae shove
your granny aff a bus.
Oh you cannae
shove yer granny,
Cause she's yer
mammy's mammy
You cannae shove
yer granny aff a bus.

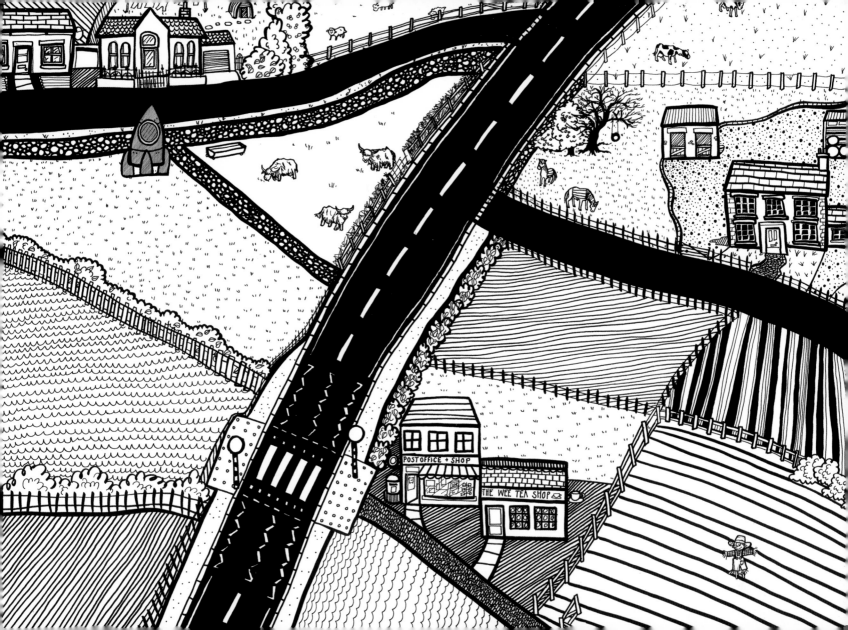

What you should know about crossing the road with pre-school children

Just talking about **stop**, **look** and **listen** isn't enough.

Young children find it difficult to stop and will be too easily distracted to properly look and listen for traffic.

Children aren't ready to cross a road by themselves until they are at least **8 years of age**.

Real learning comes from real experiences.

Every time you cross a road with a young child, the child will learn from **what you do and what you say.**

Every time.

If you take risks when crossing the road, the child with you **won't** learn to Go Safe.